albert is pretty pretty ugly.

you mess with the best You
die like the rest. by albert You

The one and only

Albert is one of a kind

ARCTIC OCEAN

The trading post

first calf is born

Here we
crossed the river

Here we crossed the fjord

THE FJORD

*Here we met
the lemmings

The tents of our siida

My tent

Pantry tree
Main tent

Shallow stream
with the skins

To grazing grounds

To Kautokeino

VIDDA

VIDDA

Here the ice
cracked

VIDDA

Here we leave
the sledges

Grazing grounds
of the big herd

Calving place of our reindeer

A.M. JAUSS

ALSO BY SONIA AND TIM GIDAL

My Village in Austria

My Village in Denmark

My Village in England

My Village in Greece

My Village in India

My Village in Ireland

My Village in Israel

My Village in Italy

My Village in Norway

My Village in Spain

My Village in Switzerland

My Village in Yugoslavia

Sons of the Desert

FOLLOW THE REINDEER

BY SONIA AND TIM GIDAL

PANTHEON BOOKS NEW YORK

1435

1

My name is Anders Oskal. I am a nomad. I live in Lapland, high above the Arctic Circle.

Lapland belongs to three countries: Norway, Finland, and Sweden. I live in the Norwegian part of Lapland.

I was born in a tent, on a dark winter day. In winter the sun does not rise above the horizon for seven long weeks in our Arctic country.

When I was three months old, my mother and father told me, they took me with them on spring migration. They wrapped me tightly in reindeer skins, and fastened me down in my birchwood cradle with sealskin straps. We travelled in sledges, and the sledges were drawn by reindeer.

We followed our big reindeer herd for three weeks, until we came to the hills on the coast of the Arctic Ocean. There we found grazing grounds for our reindeer, and stayed all summer. Late in fall we migrated back to our winter grounds.

Our people have a saying: "It is better to move than to stay in one place." For eight months every year we wander with our herd. Only from Christmas to Easter do we stay near our church village, Kautokeino. There we meet our friends and relatives, and we buy our supplies in the village, and people get married, and babies are christened. My three younger sisters go to school in Kautokeino, for four months each year.

Last week our whole family went to church for my baby brother's christening. He was born two months ago, and he was named Johan. Soon it will be *his* turn to travel in a cradle.

I have another brother, Isak. He is three years old, and he makes the reindeer jumpy, running among them with his lasso. He is very good at lassoing. Nobody is safe from him.

I have one older sister named Inga, but I am the oldest son in our family of ten.

I have my own dog and Inga has hers. Every grown-up Lapp has his own dog. Mine is called Tshupp. He is always with me. I couldn't guard the reindeer without his help. He scented the wolves, last week, long before I would have noticed them. When I saw him sniffing into the wind, his hair bristling, we hid deep in the snow. When the wolves came near, Tshupp and I cut off their retreat.

One wolf jumped at Tshupp, and I hit him on the head with my stick as hard as I could. The wolf turned on me, but I caught his teeth with the stick in my left hand, and with the knife in my right hand I killed him.

When we came back to our tents with the dead wolf, Father praised me. "You are a good herdsman, Anders," he said. "You killed your first wolf—now you are old enough to lead a string of sledge reindeer on the next spring migration!"

"Thank you, Atche," I said. I call my father Atche and my mother Eddny in our language.

I am very happy. This is a great honor for me.

I saw the sun today for the first time in seven weeks! People came running from all the tents; everybody laughed and sang with joy, because the sun had returned to us at last, after the long weeks of darkness.

We all stood on a hill to watch the golden disk come up over the horizon, stay a few minutes, and then disappear again in a splash of red and orange colors. The sky stayed light for a long time.

Everybody talks about leaving, and we all prepare for it. My younger sisters are glad they have eight months of vacation coming again.

Farewell visitors crowd into our tent all day long. We drink many cups of coffee, and wish each other a safe migration with our reindeer. Then we put on our skis and visit our friends in *their* tents and drink many more cups of coffee until late into the night.

2

TSHUPP WAKES ME. He has pushed the tent flap aside with his paws, and now he licks my face. He wants me to get up.

Tshupp and Isak sleep with me in the same tent, but they must have gone out long ago—Isak isn't under his reindeer fur any more.

I throw off my fur covers. It is so very cold that I put on two pairs of reindeer pants: first short ones with the fur inside next to my skin; then my long breeches with the fur outside. This keeps me warm and dry.

I stuff senna grass into my skallers, my reindeer-hide boots. Senna grass is much warmer than the wool socks the Norwegians wear.

My skallers are both the same shape so it doesn't matter which one I put on the right foot and which one on the left.

Outside I wash my face with a handful of snow. Isak comes running. "Anders, look!" he calls. "Atche is coming with the reindeer. We're going to the weddings!"

"Buore Baive!" I say to Atche and to my sister Inga, who start harnessing the reindeer.

"Buore Baive!" they answer. "Good day!" And Inga says, "We have all eaten already, lazybones. You will be late for the weddings."

"You can start," I call back. "I am going to eat and still be in the village before you!"

In the tent I eat the bannugakko, a pancake of reindeer blood and flour, which Eddny has fried for me, and she pours me a big bowl of coffee.

Outside I see Inga wind a red-and-blue ribbon around the neck of a reindeer and harness it with a head-halter to her sleigh. But this isn't her own reindeer. It is Atche's beautiful Twist-Horn, our best sledge animal, the fastest runner we have.

Ah, that's it! Inga wants to show off to her friends, and she must have begged Atche to give her Twist-Horn today for the ride to the church.

Ellen has already harnessed Gray Long-Horn to my sledge. I jump in, take the sealskin reins, and call to Inga, "Shall we race to the village?"

"May we, Atche?" asks Inga. "I want to show my brother he is *not* as fast a racer as he thinks he is."

Atche grins and says, "Yes, daughter, teach him a lesson if you can. But be careful, do not strain Twist-Horn when you go fast."

"Hoiah!" we shout, and off we go. I have a good head start and I leave Inga behind me. I keep the reins on the right side of Gray Long-Horn. When I want him to go faster I pull the rein, but I do it gently.

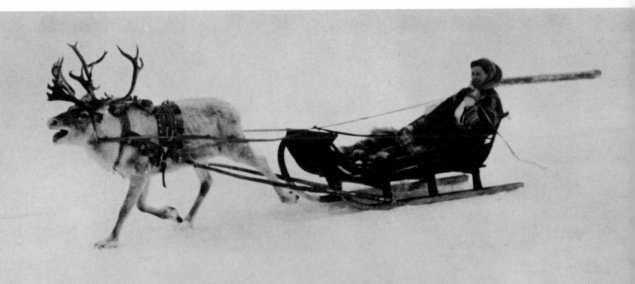

The icy wind cuts into my face. We dash over the hard snow crust as fast as the wind itself. "Hoiah!" I shout back to Inga, and wave to her.

"Hoiah!" she calls. She is almost even with me. How did *that* happen? "Hoiah! Hoiah! On! On!" I shout to my reindeer, and pull the reins.

"Hoiah! Hoiah!" Inga cries out—and off she goes right in front of my nose. I do not like it one bit, but after all, Twist-Horn is Atche's fastest reindeer.

I try hard to catch up, and race after Inga. I pass tents and a few huts. In the huts live Lapps who have settled down for good and do not go on migration any more with reindeer herds. I would never live in a hut, not in summer and not in winter, nor would anyone in my family.

Now I am only ten or twelve reindeer lengths behind Inga's sleigh. I come closer and closer to her, but then we arrive at the village, and we stop at the church.

"Well done, Twist-Horn. You won!" I say.

"Well done, *Inga*, you mean," says my sister, and she slaps me on the shoulder.

Many people have come to the weddings. We Lapps go to church only between Christmas and Easter. Today four couples are going to be married. Everybody wears white skallers and his best belt.

My family has driven up in the meantime. They all travelled together in two sledges; even little Johan in his birchwood cradle came along.

We form a double line, each pair holding hands. The bridegrooms and brides walk in the middle of the line. I walk with Isak.

I watch the sacristan in the belfry hit the bell with a stick. He hits it slowly at first, and then faster and faster until it sounds like one long-drawn-out tone.

Atche and Eddny walk in front of me.

"Look up there, Christine," says Atche to my mother. "The snow on the church roof is melting. We had better get ready to leave for the coast. We'll start tomorrow morning, I think."

When the snow melts on the church roof it's a sign for us to start the spring migration. After the first thaw the top snow freezes into a hard crust at night, and then the sledges travel easily over the frozen surface. The reindeer don't sink in even when pulling a big load.

Leaving tomorrow! So I was right when I thought the reindeer were restless yesterday. They always feel it when it is time for them to migrate to the coast.

Our church is small and there isn't enough room for everybody. But today our family goes in, all ten of us, because our cousin Lars is to be married.

Behind Lars and his bride their dogs walk right into church with them. They are quiet; they know very well how to behave when they are told.

All newly wed couples are allowed to bring their dogs to church. The dogs are our friends. We couldn't be nomad Lapps without them, we couldn't survive without them, and when we celebrate they celebrate with us.

Cousin Mikkel sits at a table at the church door, and on the way out everybody tells him what his wedding present is. Mikkel writes it down in a big book. Atche and Eddny give Cousin Lars a year-old white reindeer.

After church Atche calls my sister Ellen and me. "I think we will leave tomorrow," he says. "Drive home now, you two, but do not race this time, Anders. Bring the sledge reindeer to our tents. This morning I separated them from the big herd."

Ellen makes a sad face, and Atche says:

"I am sorry you cannot stay. I will follow you soon. We will just have a bite of the wedding cake, and drink to the health of Lars and his bride. I'll bring you each a big piece of cake."

Ellen and I drive home fast. Tshupp runs behind.

"Why couldn't Inga go with you?" asks Ellen. "She is older than I."

"I suppose Atche wants you to start handling reindeer on your own," I answer. "There just are not enough grownups in our family yet. You know it yourself. And girls, girls, girls! More girls in our family than tents. Anyway, Inga is busy today."

"Busy indeed! Is she going to marry that fish-head Ture?"

Now I get annoyed, and I cut Ellen short. "Dappat!" I tell her. "Keep quiet. I like Ture. He is my friend."

8

At the tents I tie the reindeer to a dwarf birch. We take puukos along, our big knives, and we sling the lassos around our shoulders.

"Tshupp, you stay here and watch Gray Long-Horn," I say.

We ski for two hours over the hard snow. At last I see our sledge reindeer grazing. Ellen and I are both thirsty, so we eat some snow. I let it melt in my mouth first, as the reindeer do. It tastes better that way.

Our reindeer can smell out the moss through a three-foot layer of snow. They dig for it with their sharp fore-hoofs, and while they eat they throw the snow behind them. Their noses are deep in the snow.

The reindeer always face into the wind, and they catch the wolves' scent for miles ahead. On windy days we stand guard at the back of the herd in case the wolves should sneak up from behind.

Our reindeer did not get enough moss this winter; they are a bit thin, and not as strong as they should be for the hard migration to the coast. Fourteen of our animals have died of hunger.

Through my field glasses I can see the big herds. Our animals are there, and the two herds of my uncles.

Ellen and I lasso one after the other of our eight sledge reindeer. They kick with their legs and butt with their antlers, and it is hard work to harness them all.

We tie the animals together with thongs, one behind the other, and each of us leads a string of four back to the siida. The siida—that's our

family and our reindeer and our dogs, and our tents, everything together.

It is getting dark already and we have just started on our way home. "Look, Anders!" Ellen calls in a frightened voice, and she points into the dark. "Wolves' eyes!" I grab my knife and swing around on my skis, but I don't see anything.

The reindeer follow us meekly now. The only sound comes from their split hoofs; they give off a crunching noise when they strike against each other.

"Where is Atche?" Ellen asks me. "He said he would come out and help us."

"I don't know, Ellen. Something must have happened. Atche always keeps his promise. Let's hurry."

At last I see a faint light. It comes from the fire in our tent.

"Here we are," I say. Ellen has worked hard and must be even more tired than I am.

Now I hear the tinkling of Twist-Horn's bell. Tshupp runs up to me, barking with pleasure. We tie the animals loosely to the birch trees and step inside the tent. My face is frozen stiff. I can't even wrinkle my nose.

"Buore Baive!" we greet each other, and Ellen and I lie down near the fire. Eddny takes the kettle from the hearth fire. She has coffee ready for us, and a big chunk of reindeer leg.

Johan is asleep in his cradle. Atche isn't in, but all the others are there. They seem worried, and Eddny keeps her eye on the tent flap.

"Where is Atche?" I ask. "Is he still at the wedding party?"

"No, he is not," Eddny answers.

"Where is he? What happened?"

Eddny tells the story:

"We were all sitting at the wedding meal, and Grandfather was singing and telling jokes. We laughed and laughed and he sang one song after the other. Suddenly Uncle Nils opened the door. He didn't even take off his skis. 'Gumpi lae bottsuin!' he shouted. 'The wolves are in the herd!'

"'Gumpi lae bottsuin!' everybody shouted. We ran out and got rifles and clubs from the sledges. The men put on their skis and rushed off with the dogs. We others returned home, each family to its own tent.

"We have been packing all this time. You know we want to leave tomorrow if the weather holds. Now we are waiting for Atche to come back. I hope he doesn't bring bad news."

"Sing something about the wolves," Anna begs. "Curse them, so they will leave our reindeer alone."

I take a copper string from my kofte, the long blue woolen blouse I wear. I always have copper string with me for trapping partridges. I knot one end to the sewing machine. I hold the other end and pluck it with my free hand while I sing. I learned the melodies from Atche and Grandfather, but the words I always make up myself, as every Lapp does. We call this Yoiking.

> *Kumpi don ednak vahag lek dakekam . . .*
> *I curse you, wolf, flee far away,*
>   *Voia Voia Nana.*
> *In our lands no longer stay,*
>   *Voia Voia Nana.*
> *Run away now, run for life,*
>   *Voia Nana Voia.*
> *I'll kill you with my hunter's knife!*
>   *Voia Nana Voia.*
>   *Voia Voia Nana Nana,*
>   *Voia Voia Nana Nana.*

Suddenly the tent flap is pushed aside, and Atche stands there with his pipe in his mouth. He looks happy. I see from his eyes that he must have killed a wolf.

"Buurist! Buurist!" we call to him. "God save you!"

Atche answers, "Buurist!" and he slaps everybody on the shoulder. That is all he says. He just sits down, takes tobacco from his pouch, and fills his pipe. I light it for him with a burning splinter.

Eddny passes him a plate with steaming meat. On another plate she gives cooked reindeer feet to Atche's dog Ran.

"You must eat," she says. But Atche shakes his head. Too exhausted to eat or even to speak, he stretches out on a reindeer skin and smokes. Ran has eaten. Now he lies down next to Atche and falls asleep at once.

Isak is the first one to ask a question. "Is the bad wolf dead, Atche?"

And Atche answers slowly: "Yes, Isak. Four wolves are dead, and one or two must have been wounded. We saw the blood trails. The reindeer are safe again."

"All?" asks Anna.

"No. Not all, Anna. The wolves killed seven reindeer. Two-year-old Gray Crooked-Horn was among them, and four-year-old One-Horn White-Belly . . . and six-year-old Nine-Horns Spotty-Flanks. . . ."

Marit starts crying quietly. Nine-Horns Spotty-Flanks was one of her four reindeer. She got it as a present from Atche and Eddny on the day her first tooth appeared, six years ago.

"The wolves were wild with hunger," Atche says. "Uncle Nils' boys could not drive them away even with rifle shots. They always came back. First they stood far off. It was a pack of six, and they circled and circled the herd from afar for hours, to frighten them into scattering so they could attack the reindeer singly. Uncle Nils' boys and the dogs kept the herd together, and killed one wolf who had come close. But they could not be everywhere at the same time, and Uncle Nils had skied off to the village to warn us.

"The herd moved close together and started milling around in a circle so they could defend themselves better. When it got darker, the wolves came close. They attacked from different sides, and then the reindeer panicked. Many scattered and fled. That was when the wolves could jump them one by one, and kill so many. It happened just before we arrived.

"But then, of course, we eight men were too many for the wolves to escape. We went after them on our skis and killed three more— the others escaped in the darkness. We skied after them, and I think we must have wounded one or two.

"Now you know why I could not come to help you with the sledge reindeer, Ellen," Atche says. "You must have worked very hard." He takes off his four-cornered cap and out of two corners he takes two huge pieces of wedding cake, topped with cloudberries and wrapped in birch bark. The berries are squashed and the cake looks awful after all the bumping around on Atche's head, but it tastes delicious.

Atche wants to sleep. He stretches out on the skins.

"Marit, the first calf born this spring will be yours," he says. Then he turns over and is asleep in an instant. No noise can wake him now, but he will wake up the minute he wants to. In winter, and during migration, we rarely sleep more than three or four hours at a stretch. We have to take turns watching over the herd. But in summer I can sleep twelve and fifteen hours at a time.

Isak sleeps, too. But we others start carrying things to the sledges. It is long past midnight, but now that spring is here the night is no longer quite as dark as it is in winter.

I carry the sewing machine out to Eddny's sledge. The bell around Twist-Horn's neck jingles, and I hear him breathe hard in the cold.

"The Northern Lights!" Inga cries. The horizon flickers with a curtain of flames, growing brighter and brighter. The wall of light waves back and forth, red at the bottom, white in the middle, and green on

16

top. Then a row of fireballs suddenly shoots across the sky, and all the snow hills glow with light and color. The brilliant fires seem to come nearer and nearer—now they are right over our heads; the whole sky becomes a giant blanket of many colors. Back and forth, up and down it moves, the patterns ever changing.

Anna and Marit cover their faces with their hands. I do not like the Northern Lights myself—they frighten me.

Eddny is not afraid of them. "Look," she says, "the lights are over the northern horizon. It means a cold spell. The snow crust will be hard and we will have a good start tomorrow—just as Atche said we would."

The frozen reindeer joints are wrapped in skins. We carry the heavy chunks to the sledges and tie them on. The leather bags with sugar we wrap in canvas. All our chests with clothing, tools, provisions, and toys were packed in the afternoon by Eddny and my sisters. They have even taken down the sleeping tents and stored them on the sledges.

Tonight we all sleep in the big tent. All the floor space is taken up by my sisters and brothers, Atche and Eddny, and the four dogs. It is very crowded but nice and warm. Tshupp curls up behind me and warms my back.

Just before I fall asleep I see Atche get up and leave the tent.

ATCHE WAKES US AT DAWN. We huddle around the fire for a last meal of coffee, bannugakko, blood soup, and smoked reindeer ribs. I cut pieces of the meat with my knife and dip them into coffee—it tastes best that way.

Then we are ready to leave. Eddny wraps pot and kettle into a special bundle for her sledge, so they will be handy when we stop. She also keeps in her sledge enough provisions for one day: dried meat and flatbread which she had made over the fire; coffee, of course, and sugar —we drink many cups of sweet coffee every day. And she also has with her cleaned reindeer stomachs filled with dried milk and cheese.

Inga and Ellen harness the animals to the sledges. Atche climbs up the ladder to the top of the tent and unfastens the ropes that tie the canvas to the poles. I pull the canvas down with a long stick, then we take the poles apart. We fasten them to the last sledge of the second string of six—the tent sledge.

Atche leads the first six animals with their sledges. A sealskin strap is fastened from the back of every sledge to the harness of the following reindeer. Six sledges are always tied together this way. We call it a string, and our caravan of twelve sledges is a raido. I lead the second string.

Eddny sits in the second sledge with Isak and little Johan in his cradle. Berit, Marit, and Anna have the third sledge to themselves, and Eddny's dog Tsalma rides with them. Tsalma is too heavy now to run in the snow—in a few weeks she will have puppies.

In the next three sledges are the provisions and a few empty boxes for the bags of extra coffee and flour and salt we are going to buy today. Butter, made from reindeer milk, is in a birchwood barrel.

We killed thirty-six reindeer this winter for food, and we use every part of them, not only the meat and the skins. From the bones and antlers we make knives and belt buckles, and boxes for matches and needles. The reindeer sinews we dry and separate into single threads. Then Eddny and my sisters soften them in their mouths, and by rolling two threads against their cheeks for a long time they fuse them into a single thread. They use them for sewing our boots and our winter coats of reindeer fur.

Atche and Eddny make sausages from reindeer blood mixed with meat. The sausages and cheese will last us all through the summer.

18

Some of the blood is frozen into big cubes. We keep the cubes in buckets packed tightly with snow until we need them for soup or bannugakko.

Inga sits in the last of my sledges. She watches out for things that might fall off. Behind her trots Tshupp, and if Inga misses anything *he* always spots it, and then he runs to me to bark his report.

Atche pulls Twist-Horn forward with a little jerk. Twist-Horn starts and pulls the others after him. They struggle to get loose from the string, but Twist-Horn is stronger and pulls until the others understand what he wants, and they all walk and pull in the same direction, at the same speed.

My string follows Atche's. We are off!

I look back. I see the last heap of brushwood on the hearth stones. On the place where our winter tent stood for so long the smoke still rises high.

I begin to yoik with joy:

> *It's wonderful to move again!*
> *Voia Voia Nana.*
> *How beautifully my reindeer pulls!*
> *Voia Voia Nana.*
> *And now we wander to the coast!*
> *Voia Voia Nana.*
> *The big herd will soon be with us!*
> *Voia Voia Voia.*

We come to the village and stop at Nils Helander's store. It is so warm in there that we leave our thick fur coats on the bench outside.

"Buore Baive, Nils Helander! Good day," everybody says. We shake hands with him and clap him on the back, and he claps us on the shoulder.

Atche buys thirty pounds of roasted coffee beans, twenty pounds of margarine, two twenty-pound bags of sugar, twenty pounds of salt, forty pounds of potatoes, and twenty pounds of flour.

Inga and Ellen bring two old sugar sacks into the store, and take out forty pairs of reindeer gloves and fifty pairs of reindeer boots. We made them all during the last four months.

Nils Helander looks over every pair carefully. Then he writes in his black account book what he owes us for them, and what we owe him for the provisions we have bought. All through the winter we bring him reindeer skins and gloves, skallers, and knife handles and buttons that we make from the antlers. He buys from every Lapp family around here. He often travels in his reindeer sledges to the town of Alta on the Arctic Ocean. There he sells his wares to traders from the

ports of Bergen and Oslo, and buys provisions for his store right off the boats and ships in the harbor.

Atche and I carry the sacks and bags outside and stack them in the sledges.

Inga buys red ribbons for her new hood. I guess they are for her wedding next spring.

Atche now brings in a huge side of smoked reindeer and hands it to Nils Helander, and he gets tobacco for it. Then they figure out together how the year's accounts stand. Nils Helander has it all down in his book, but Atche has it all in his head. He remembers every single figure. Finally Atche sells Nils the seven reindeer that the wolves killed yesterday. This time it is Nils Helander who has to pay.

"Anders, Isak is in the barrel where the skins are soaking," Marit calls to me. She stands with Berit in the store and sees it just in time.

I rush out and grab Isak by the bottom of his pants and swing him high into the air before I let him down.

"What are you trying to do, Isak?" I ask him. "Get the skins out of the barrel, or drink the birch-bark water?"

"My lasso," Isak cries, "I want my lasso." He has lost it and is now searching everywhere for it. The barrel is full of skins soaking in birch-bark water. That makes the skins soft.

In the store Eddny buys candies, and chocolate, and fruit, and nuts for everyone. I buy the last two numbers of the *Nuorttanaste, The Polar Star.* Our newspaper comes out every week. It is written in our Samic language.

I can read Norwegian too, but not well. Samic I understand much better. Other people call us Lapps. It is a Norwegian word, but our real name is Samers. It means "human beings."

For the next weeks until we come to the trading post on the big fjord, my two copies of *The Polar Star* will be the only news we have.

We shake hands with Nils Helander.

"Mana derivan," he says. "Go in peace, you and your whole siida." He shakes hands with all of us and wishes us and our reindeer and our dogs a safe migration.

"Bazza derivan," we answer. "Stay in peace."

When we leave the store, our koftes are almost bursting with the many things we have bought and stuffed inside. We have no pockets in our trousers and koftes, so we stuff everything into the opening of our blouses and things drop down until they are stopped by the belt. The lower I wear my belt the more I can stuff into the kofte. It's a much safer place than any pocket; nothing can fall out and get lost when we sit on the ground or when we cross the rivers.

Our raido moves on again. Soon we are on the wide plains, the vidda. I can hardly keep my eyes open, the sunlight on the snow is so strong.

Atche gives the sign to stop. This is where we wait for our reindeer. My Uncles Nils and Johan will drive them here. All through the winter the three herds of Atche and his two brothers have been grazing together, but during the last two weeks we have separated them. Every family takes its own herd to the grazing grounds on the hilly coast.

By their earmarks I can distinguish every one of our eight hundred and twenty-four reindeer. At the fall roundups every fawn has the mark of its owner cut into both earlaps with a knife. So we always know which belongs to whom.

Every Lapp has his own design for these earmarks. All designs are registered with the District Court in Kautokeino village. Nobody in the whole of Lapland uses the same earmarks as anybody else.

I scan the horizon through my telescope, but before I see the reindeer Atche calls out: "Hoja! Hoja! Get up! The herd is coming." He doesn't need a telescope, and now I too hear the crunching sound made by the onrushing feet of many hundred reindeer. Stretching my neck to see them come over the hill, I fall backward into my sledge with a rude bump. My reindeer go wild when they hear the herd. They dash off madly and race in a wide circle, around and around. I have dropped the reins and can't stop them. My brothers and sisters look on and laugh.

Atche speeds toward them on his skis, and when my leading animal passes he throws himself at its head and with a powerful pull jerks the antlers to the side. The animal loses its balance and falls. All the others are jerked to a stop and the sledges pile up behind them. Two are overturned, and the tent poles scattered on the ground. Inga and Ellen help me put them back, still laughing.

Atche speeds off to meet his brothers, and when he reaches the herd he takes the rope of the leading reindeer from Uncle Nils.

My uncles come over and shake hands with all of us, and we clap each other on the back.

"Arrive in good time for the calving!" they wish us, and Uncle Nils says, "I will visit you in summer. Buurist! God save you!" And they ski back to their own herds.

Atche leads the first reindeer. Behind him comes the most important reindeer of our whole herd, the Follower. He is called "Follower" because he follows the leading animal of his own free will. This sets an example for all the other reindeer and they in turn follow it. It is our most valuable animal. Behind the Follower comes a small group of tamed oxen and does. They keep close to the Follower, and together they form the leadership of the whole herd.

The reindeer move in tight formation, but there are always stragglers. Atche's dog Ran and Inga's dog Benne drive them forward into the herd again.

Most of the oxen and bulls have lost their antlers in winter. But the does still have theirs. They need antlers to protect themselves before their fawns are born. Later in spring they too will shed them.

I see all my sixteen animals in the herd. Inga already has twenty of her own, and Ellen has nine. Marit has only three now, after Nine-Horns Spotty-Flanks was killed by the wolves. Even little Johan owns a reindeer, a small white one. My uncles gave it to him as a christening present.

The reindeer are our only real property, and we take good care of them during the dangerous winter and migration time.

All day we travel over hills and through valleys. Sometimes a sledge overturns on a steep hill and pulls the other sledges with it. We fall out of the sledges and roll downhill, and the reindeer fall in a sideways somersault. But little harm is done. We get the reindeer back on their feet, repair the damage to the sledges, pack everything up again, and travel on.

After many hours we come to the great river. We follow its course and travel on its frozen, snow-covered surface until it turns west. Then we go north over the high mountains and viddas.

We eat bread and butter and sausage while we travel. There will be no rest until late in the night.

Ellen and Inga are asleep in their sledges behind me. The younger ones are asleep too, tucked deep down into their furs. Only Eddny and I are awake, driving the sledge reindeer forward. We follow Atche, who glides over the snow leading the herd. The herd follows because the animals know the trek is taking it to the hills on the coast of the Arctic Ocean where the reindeer were born. Atche guides the animals, but the reindeer follow him only because he leads them in the direction they want to go. "I lead the herd," Atche often says, "and the herd leads *me*."

Eddny gives me a sign. I wake Inga, and she runs to the front sledge and takes over the reins from Eddny. She skis in front for a while and leads the raido while Eddny nurses little Johan. We must not stop between resting places but must move on as long as the snow is hard enough and the going good for the sledges and reindeer. We must cross the lakes and rivers before the ice cracks. If we do not reach the coast before the snow thaws, we will get bogged down in the slush. We must reach the summer grazing grounds before the fawns are born.

It is very cold, and it is snowing. Gray dusk has settled over the land, enveloping us. We keep close to the herd now. I cannot see where the snow-covered ground ends and the horizon begins. I am frozen stiff. The cold has crept through my fur coat and my clothing, and bites into my bones.

Atche waves to us with his ski pole from the crest of a near slope.

Behind the crest is a snow field with dwarf birch trees. They keep off the strong winds and the snow drifts. The snow isn't deep here, and the reindeer will find enough moss. The evening sun has suddenly come through the clouds again. Here we will stay the short night.

I stop in front of Atche. We unharness the sledge reindeer. They are tired and hungry after their strenuous first day's march, and they graze for fresh moss among the little birches. I get a piece of fat reindeer cheese and rub it on my half-frozen cheeks, to make sure I don't get chilblains. Eddny does the same to her face, then wakes all the children and rubs their cold cheeks.

25

Eddny and Inga clear a wide circle in the snow for the tent. Together we take the poles and canvas from the sledges, and the wooden chest with the kitchen things. Everybody is busy. Marit brings snow for making coffee. Atche and I put up the tent. I bring dry birchwood from a sledge and make a fire. Then I cut down a few birch trees for tomorrow. We always make sure of having wood for the next day.

Atche has hung the hearth chain on the smoke pole. With a hatchet Inga chops off a piece of frozen reindeer blood and throws it in the big pot. When it melts Atche takes marrow bones from a bag and drops them in. He tastes the soup—he hasn't even taken his lasso off his shoulders yet. He adds snow from a bucket, and small pieces of meat, and salt. He watches the soup while he stirs.

"Atche, please don't let the soup get too thick," I say. Nobody likes thick soup. We have a saying: "When the soup gets too thick poverty is waiting for you." Atche looks at me smiling, and answers, "You have learned that saying, haven't you? I will tell you another one: He whose bootlaces come untied will be teased by the girls." And with that, he looks at my feet.

My bootlaces are untied again—now of all times! Everybody laughs, and I can't even answer.

We are all very hungry, and at last the soup is ready and Atche ladles it out to us. After the soup we eat sausages and bread with reindeer butter, and we cut pieces from a large reindeer rib, roasting them over the fire on the tips of our knives before we eat them.

Ellen and Marit wash four dishes with snow and fill them with soup and reindeer feet for the dogs.

My stomach feels warm again, and we all stretch out on the skins. Eddny says, "Take off your boots, all of you."

One after the other we take the senna grass from our boots and give it to Eddny. She feels the heat of the fire with one hand, while she turns the grass with the other until it is dry again.

We cut the senna grass in the fall; it grows thickly on the banks of the fjords. I line my boots evenly with the grass again and put them back on. Eddny always says, "As you line your boots, so you will walk!"

Everybody is settling down to sleep, but little Johan is crying. Inga rocks his cradle and gives him a piece of dried reindeer meat. He sucks it, but then he starts crying again. Inga sings to him:

Nana galka nokka
Now the child must go to sleep!
Nana nana nana
Nana galka nokka
Now the child must go to sleep!
Nana nana nana. . . .

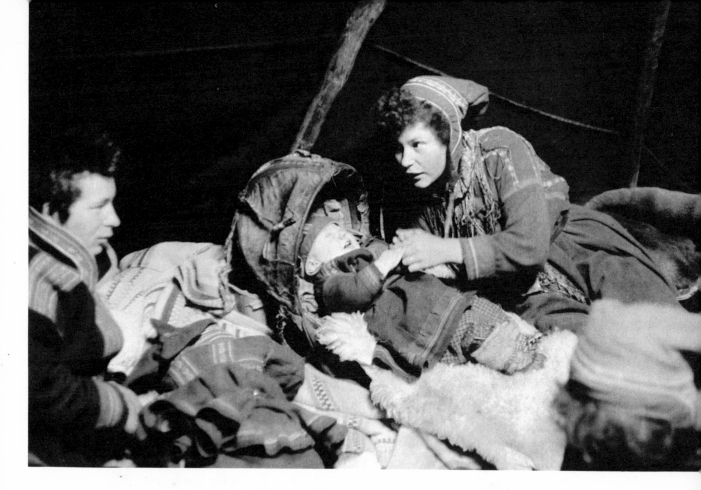

Back and forth she rocks him, until at last Johan is fast asleep.

I made Johan's cradle, from a piece of birchwood. The hood I made of birchwood too, and lined it with a few layers of leather. They protect his head when he is thrown about in the sledge, and when he hangs in his cradle over the back of a reindeer.

I go out to look after the sledge reindeer. They lie quietly in the snow, chewing their cud. Atche brings some furs to the tent.

Inside the tent it is now quiet and dark. The fire on the hearth has burned itself out, and only the embers are glowing.

I lie down on a skin near the entrance and pull another skin over me. Inga is outside with the three dogs. She has the first watch against wolves. Then she will wake Atche, and Atche will later wake *me*.

4

FOR THREE WEEKS we wander over the fjells and viddas—up and down the hills, over frozen lakes and rivers, through the valleys, always getting nearer the coast.

The snow crust holds up well for many days. But when the weather gets warmer and the snow becomes soft in the daytime we change our way of living: we sleep during the day and travel by night. The nights are still cold enough for the snow to freeze, and then we push on, twelve hours, sometimes sixteen hours without rest. "Forward!" says Atche. "Forward to the coast before the great thaw sets in."

Often we sleep only a few hours in our sledges, without taking time to pitch a tent. We eat only before we go to sleep and before starting out.

The reindeer get weak from the long marches, and often they don't find enough moss. Three of the animals have become so exhausted that they can't keep up with the others, and during a snowstorm they disappear. We stop and search for them, but they are gone—and we have to push on. We are now high in the mountains, and every hour is precious.

The next day four animals die of exhaustion, then another three. The reindeer are sinking up to their bellies in the soft snow, and the going is very hard.

The following day we come to the big lake. The ice under the snow still seems thick and strong. We hack holes in the ice two feet deep before water shows.

We cross the lake at a good speed. Suddenly Atche gives a warning shout and waves us back. "Voi! Voi! Voi!" he cries. "Turn back! The ice is breaking!"

I make a wide semicircle, and bring my six sledges safely back to land. Eddny stops, turns her string around, and races back. Then I run over to Atche and help him turn back the herd. The dogs all help too, but the reindeer become frightened and try to break in every direction.

All of us, except little Johan of course, run to the herd and shout and drive them away from the crack in the ice. But now the ice under the herd itself begins to crack with an awful noise. The Follower is in the middle of the panicky herd.

Father swings his lasso, which flies straight and catches the Follower around the neck.

"Quick, Anders," Atche cries, and I speed to him. Together we pull the struggling Follower out of the herd toward land. Then at last many of the reindeer turn after him, and the others we round up with the help of the dogs.

The cracks in the ice widen before our very eyes. Crossing the lake is no longer possible. But the siida is safe: our family and the reindeer and the dogs are all unharmed.

We skirt the lake through slush and soft snow, and then again follow the big river.

At last we see the coast. Far below us, to the west, are low hills and fjords, and farther out stretches an endless gray sea—the Arctic Ocean. We have made it!

Now we can safely rest before beginning the difficult descent. For two days we sleep and eat. Then we start down from the steep heights. We wind ropes around the runners of our sledges to keep them from sliding into the sledge reindeer. Often our sledges overturn and crash down the steep slopes, pulling the animals off their feet. Sledges and reindeer roll over and over. But the animals quickly get to their feet again and wait patiently while we repair the sledges.

Halfway down, near the coast, the snow has melted away and the sledges have become useless. Yesterday we left them behind. We bound them together and weighted them down with tree trunks. In fall, when we go back inland, we will find our sledges again.

We load the sledge reindeer with all the bags and chests and tents and poles and our few remaining provisions. They are now our pack reindeer. We divide the loads evenly on their backs, forty pounds on each side. They cannot carry more than eighty pounds each. Isak is the only one to ride on a pack animal. The cradle with little Johan hangs from one side of a reindeer.

We have crossed many rivers, and now we wander along the fjord until we come to the last one. In the distance, across the fjord, I see the hills and valleys of our grazing grounds. Up there, in the cool hills, are the calving places for our does.

The river flows swiftly. We put stones into our koftes to make us heavy. The stones will give us more steadiness in the current.

First we get the herd across. The lead reindeer does not like the icy water, and I help Atche pull it in. It looks ugly now without its beautiful antlers. In a few weeks they will start growing again.

Atche holds a long stick in his left hand and probes the river bed, looking for rocks. Inga and Ellen keep watch farther downstream to see that no animal is carried away by the strong current.

My leather trousers keep the water out even though it reaches to my waist. The swift current makes me lose ground a few times.

The herd crosses safely to the other side. Now the pack animals are led across. I walk with the tent reindeer. The water presses against the long poles, throwing the animal off balance. I lean against it to help it push forward.

Inga has Johan in his cradle slung around her shoulders, and Eddny carries Isak in her arms.

In the middle of the stream Eddny gives a warning shout. One of the reindeer has fallen. I wade forward and get it on its feet again. Meanwhile a few packs have fallen off and are floating downstream. I jump after them and catch a bundle. But the two canvas bundles that held my tent are carried away by the swift current.

I shiver with cold, but there is more work to be done. Together with Inga, I help Anna and Marit across the stream. We grasp one another in a double wrist hold and walk across in a chain. Inga goes first, then come the two younger sisters, and I go last, with Berit on my shoulders; Berit carries her doll on *her* shoulder.

We make many more trips across the river, with the sugar and flour bags, and the many small bundles.

"Oh, look!" cries Marit, and points up the slope. "A fawn!" There it is; the first fawn has been born. The mother doe nudges the little red fawn and the baby gets up, and falls again. It tries again and again,

34

until it stands stiffly on its legs, as thin as little sticks. The front legs can't carry the fawn yet, and it often falls on its knees. But within an hour it will be hobbling beside its mother.

Marit runs over and pats the newborn fawn, and keeps close to it all the time. I wonder why Atche doesn't give it to her. He had promised her the first fawn born on spring migration, and Atche never forgets anything.

I go to the river and catch two big salmon for our next meal.

We have rested two hours, and now Atche says, "We must reach the calving places tonight. We still have to cross the fjord."

We drive the pack animals and the herd along the shore. Soon we come to the trading post and the fishermen's huts. Here the fjord is only a mile and a half wide.

On the beach lie three rowboats. They belong to the fishermen, and we can use them.

Atche pulls the lead reindeer into the water. Inga jumps into the first boat, and ties the animal on a long rope to the stern of the boat, and starts rowing. "Tjo–o! Hollo–o!" we shout, and the lead reindeer starts swimming. The Follower and all the others plunge in after it. They are good swimmers and enjoy it. The dogs drive them on from the rear.

I go with Eddny in the second boat, behind the herd, and we watch for stragglers. Marit sits next to me. She is worried about the newborn fawn. It has jumped in the water just like the older ones, its little white tail sticking out. It keeps close to its mother, and the doe swims slowly so the fawn can keep pace. But it tires quickly—it groans, rolls its eyes, and drops behind.

Quickly I row to the fawn. Eddny and Marit hold me by the belt while I lean out and pull the fawn into the boat. It is completely ex-

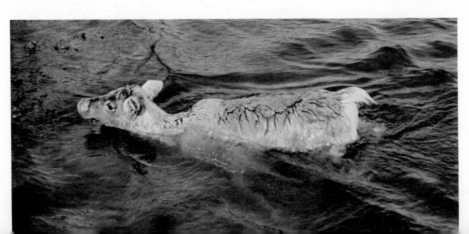

hausted and pants with terror. Marit takes it in her arms to soothe it.

We cross the fjord many times, but with the boats to carry everything and everybody it is easier than crossing the rivers.

On the other side we load the pack reindeer again. Now Atche calls Marit to him.

"Marit," he says, "I wanted the little fawn safe across the fjord before I gave it to you. It is yours now. It is a fine strong little buck."

We travel along the narrow strip of land between the sheer mountainside and the fjord. The soil is bare and stony and the going uncomfortable. The reindeer are as much in a hurry as we are. They know what lies ahead.

Suddenly the cliff opens, and there is a wide valley with gentle slopes leading upward to the mountains—the grazing grounds! A few days ago we were still wandering over snow-covered ground. But now spring is here and the budding birch trees are a pale red.

Here we part. Eddny and the others continue with the pack reindeer along the fjord to our camping site. Atche and I are to lead the herd to the high grazing grounds.

Tshupp and Ran have a hard time now. They run after the animals and drive them up the fjells. The reindeer are wild with haste. They scent the fresh moss on the hills, and they race ahead up the slopes. We can hardly keep pace with them. We run all the time, and I am sweating all over.

At last we arrive at the grazing pastures, where only dwarf birch grows, and the ground is richly covered with reindeer moss. The moss is so damp the animals won't need anything to drink now. Later in the summer, when the ground is dry, they can quench their thirst in the patches of snow that never leave the hillsides.

We separate the two hundred and sixty-four does from the herd and lead them to another grazing ground. They now stand quietly between the birch trees. Here they will have their fawns.

From this high place I can see the fjord, and through my telescope I watch Eddny and the girls unload the pack reindeer.

We have worked for three hours, and now we can leave the herd alone. The reindeer will roam freely for many weeks. No wolves come

here, and there is nothing to disturb them. They will rest peacefully all summer and grow strong again. Our spring migration is over.

Atche is happy. He starts yoiking:

> *Pastures of the little fawns,*
> *Voia Voia Nana!*
> *Oh, let my reindeer graze and prosper,*
> *Voia Nana Voia!*
> *Let there soon be more of them,*
> *Voia Nana Voia.*
> *Pastures of my little fawns,*
> *Voia Voia Nana!*
> *Let no beast, no pest come near,*
> *Voia Voia Nana Nana!*
> *Pastures of the little fawns,*
> *Voia Voia Nana!*

And then we walk straight down the hills until we come to our family.

The pack reindeer are already unharnessed, and two small tents are up. This is the third summer we have stopped at the same place. Our big hearth stones still lie in a circle on the ground.

It is a very good place to camp. Nearby, through the birch woods, runs a stream where we wash ourselves and our clothes. A fresh spring comes down a crevice and gives us our drinking water. The fjord is only a few hundred feet away and every day we fish in it.

Eddny has taken out her sewing machine. She has already cut some old pieces of canvas into the proper shape and is sewing a new tent for me and Isak because ours was lost this morning when we crossed the stream.

Atche, at last, takes off the fur coat he has been wearing much longer than any of us.

"It is my migration coat," he says, "and I take it off only when our spring migration is really over."

Eddny made it for him. She makes all our fur coats. She used six skins for it, only the best ones, and she matched them so they are all of the same thickness and color. She and Inga sewed the furs together with the sinews from reindeer legs—they are the toughest ones.

Isak watches Atche take off his coat. He has taken off his boots; that's *his* sign that spring migration is over. Isak has found his little sleigh again.

It is ten o'clock in the evening, but the sun is still high on the horizon.

Atche and I pitch the big tent. We tie one pair of curved poles together into an arch, then do the same with a second pair.

Ellen holds one arch up and I hold the second one. Atche directs us until the arches are in the right position. Then he balances the heavy crossbar above his head and pushes the ends through holes in the arch poles. The crossbar is our smoke pole, just above the hearth. To it we attach the iron bar and the chain for the kettle in such a way that they can be raised or lowered.

Ellen passes Atche a stick with fish for smoking, and he lays it across the smoke pole and the arch pole.

We stand sixteen long poles against the framework and bind them close together at the top. Then we help Atche cover the skeleton tent with two large pieces of canvas and tie them to the poles. The canvas must not reach all the way to the top. We must leave an opening to let the smoke out and the light in.

Eddny has kindled a fire, and now she throws fish and fish liver into a pot, for our first meal after spring migration.

Outside, Atche climbs a ladder to the top of the tent and fastens the canvas around the smoke pole. We always carry the ladder on migration. I made it from a dwarf birch. The ladder has only one leg to stand on. But Atche doesn't lose his balance, because the ladder leans against the canvas, and its point is pushed into the ground.

We have two openings in our big tent. But once the tent is up Atche always closes the back entrance. It is opened only when somebody in the family dies. Then the dead one is carried out through it. The big front entrance must never be used for a dead person.

Three years ago my grandmother died on the way back to Kautokeino. We dressed her in her holiday clothes, carried her out through the back opening, and laid her on the death sledge. We brought her all the way back to Kautokeino for burial.

"Marit! Anna! Veddge chazi! Fetch water!" Eddny calls. She has finished my sleeping tent, and I put it up in a few minutes. Isak helps me.

"Anders, cuolle muorre! Chop more wood! And Ellen, get twigs, and cover the ground in the tent! Berit, you can crush some sugar for the coffee! And you, Isak, get your cap full of potatoes from the storage tent!"

Eddny knows how to make us scurry around when she wants to.

I carry firewood inside. Ellen covers the ground with sweet-smelling new birch twigs. The others bring reindeer skins and the kitchen box and the low table. Then at last we sit down and wait for the meal. We are all very hungry.

Atche hangs up a tent flap on the left side of the tent. Behind the flap, he and Eddny sleep. During the day we take it off. But now Ellen sits there and feeds Johan warm reindeer milk from a bottle.

The dogs crowd around Johan. They always do when they are not busy with the herd. They love him, and now all four of them watch him drink his milk.

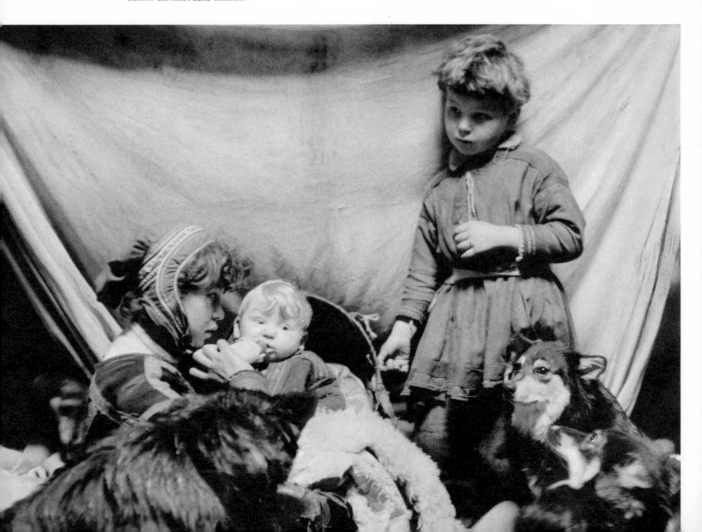

"The birch twigs around here smell sweet," Eddny says. "Much sweeter than any other birch on the whole migration."

"You always say that when we pitch summer camp," I say. I am sure the birch smells the same everywhere. Eddny just likes this place very much.

Atche takes care of the meal. He cooks the fish we have caught this morning.

In another pot fresh birch bark is being boiled. It boils for hours, until all the juices have been extracted from the bark. Eddny needs the bark water to soak our boots and the reindeer skins. The bark water makes them waterproof and supple.

Eddny sits in the boasso, the space behind the fireplace. The boasso is always on the north side of the tent, opposite the entrance. It is Eddny's place. There she keeps the big chest with foodstuff, and the dishes, and the low table where she prepares the food. Now she is holding the coffee mill on her knee and grinding the beans. Atche has

his place too. He always sits opposite Eddny, on the right side of the tent. From now on everyone has to keep strict order, and everything has its fixed place—even the calendar Eddny has just fastened to a tent pole.

Tonight we have no fresh reindeer meat. During the summer not a single reindeer will be killed for food. But we still have enough dried and smoked reindeer joints to last us a long time. And the fjord is full of fish.

Atche pours the fish soup into our aluminum plates. Everybody gets two potatoes with it, then bread and reindeer butter and a piece of smoked meat. We bought the bread at the trading post on the other side of the fjord.

The dogs get fish heads tonight, and each of them has a slice of bread with margarine.

Atche lights his pipe. He had it specially made by the pipe maker in the city of Hammerfest. He gave trader Heikki a design which he had carved in a piece of bone. Heikki goes to Hammerfest every year. He told us that it is the northernmost city in the world. He trades there, and has knives and pipes made; then he comes back and wanders from one Lapp camp to the other selling his wares.

It is late, and little Isak is falling asleep. I take him in my arms and carry him to my tent, and Tshupp follows me.

Inga and Ellen have their own sleeping tent. Marit and Anna go with Tsalma to the third one. Tsalma is now very heavy; I am sure she will have her puppies soon.

Only Berit and Johan stay with Atche and Eddny.

The moon is high in the light sky, and our reindeer are safe.

I tuck Isak into his reindeer-fur sleeping bag, and then I stretch out on the skins and fall asleep.

I wake up and look out to see how late it is. I can tell the time by the sun, but the sky is overcast, and nobody seems to be awake yet.

The dog Ran is sleeping in front of the big tent. I look at my watch. It is two o'clock in the afternoon!

We were all very tired from the migration and from the long march yesterday. In the winter nobody sleeps much because we have to watch the reindeer day and night. During spring migration we sleep even less. But in summer we sleep away every hour we can snatch.

I put my skallers on and walk over to the big tent. Atche comes out, looks at the sky, and sniffs into the wind.

46

We greet each other with "Buore Baive!"

"Anders, I am going to take the pack reindeer up to the herd," says Atche, "but the wind bothers me. Look at the clouds."

The clouds hang low and move fast.

"The wind has changed its direction three times in the last hour," Atche explains. "That makes it hard for me to find the reindeer. You know they like to wander against the wind, and they must have changed their direction several times this morning. I wonder where I will find them."

I see that Atche has been up a long time. He has felled a big birch tree, and has taken off the branches. He has cut a log five feet long and has placed it between the right entrance pole and the hearth.

I will cut a second log today, to lead from the left entrance pole to the hearth. This is the path into our tent.

The space between the two logs is for wiping our boots when we enter the tent. No stranger steps over these logs into the other parts of the tent without our invitation. But no stranger ever enters our tent without our permission anyway, and only Atche and Eddny may give the permission. Even our friends wait outside the tent until they are invited in. When the whole family leaves the camp for a day and goes up to the reindeer, or to pick cloudberries on the hills, we place one of the logs in front of the tent entrance. It is the sign that nobody is home. No visitor will enter the tent when he sees this sign.

It is time for me to chop wood again. In every siida, the oldest son is the wood chopper, and sometimes I don't like it very much. Who likes cutting wood five times a day! But it must be done, so I start cutting two birch trees into logs for the hearth fire.

We use the birch trees for many things besides firewood and twigs for covering the ground in the tent. There is the bark water Eddny boils for soaking our shoes and the reindeer hides. I bore holes into the trees and collect the juice that flows out; we use it for washing our hair and for making birch-tree wine.

I always strip the bark carefully from the trunk: I make boxes out of it, in which we store butter and berries. Or I soften the pieces in water and rub the rough side until it is smooth. Then we use it for wrapping food.

When Atche was young he made his tent of birch bark, as his father had done before him, and his grandfather and most Lapps in those days. He told me how he had cut big strips of birch bark and soaked them for many hours in hot water, and how he had to rub the outside of each piece for hours until the pieces were as flexible as leather. Then he sewed them together with reindeer sinews. In the end he had large pieces of bark, big enough to be sewn together into a tent cover.

The bark tent could be used only in summer. The winter tent was made of reindeer hides.

Now Atche wraps reindeer cheese, sausage, and bread into a piece of bark and stuffs it into his kofte. He throws the lasso over his shoulder and leads the twelve reindeer up into the fjells to the herd. Ran goes with him. I hope they find the herd soon, and Atche doesn't have to wander long in the hills with the pack reindeer on the string.

Marit comes up and looks at me. She rocks her toy cradle in her arms. Inga made it for her when I made the cradle for Johan. It is just like Johan's, only smaller. Inga decorated it with little copper nails.

"Why are you looking at me like that?" I ask. "I know you want *something*."

"I need something."

"What do you need? Birch powder for your cradle? Is your doll wet again?"

Marit imitates everything Eddny does with Johan, and when Eddny changes the birch powder in his cradle, Marit does it in hers.

Inga passes by and Marit turns to her.

"Anders is always making fun of me, Inga. I only wanted him to make something for me."

"What did you want him to make?"

"Another cradle, a big one, like Johan's."

"What for?" asks Inga.

"I need it."

"Why?"

"To put something in."

Marit never gives you a full answer. It is very annoying.

"What do you want to put in the cradle?" both of us ask her now.

"The puppies," she says.

"Oh, you stupid fish head! Why didn't you tell me!" I shout at her, and Inga and I dash over to Marit's tent.

There they are: four puppies lying by Tsalma's side and sucking. Tsalma lets them suck, then she licks them.

Marit has run after us, and she lies down and strokes Tsalma and the puppies. The puppies squeak. They can't even open their eyes yet. There is a black puppy, and there are two brown ones, and one has a white spot.

"Do I get one?" Marit asks.

"I think you will get a puppy," says Inga, "but Tsalma is Eddny's dog. Eddny will decide."

Suddenly Tsalma starts up with a growl and barks furiously.

"What's wrong with Tsalma?" Marit asks. "There are no strangers here!"

Anna has come out of her corner.

"It's all right, Tsalma, nobody is going to bother the puppies," she says. But Tsalma continues to growl.

I walk outside, and there is Isak, lying on the ground, peeping into the tent from under the canvas. Of course he would frighten Tsalma, trying to sneak in that way.

I pull Isak out by his legs. He is annoyed and shouts and struggles. But I stand him on his feet and tell him to behave. "Don't bother Tsalma now. Why didn't you come in through the front, stupid?"

"Isak wants a puppy, nobody gives me a puppy!" he cries.

"You leave the puppies alone, Isak. Don't come near them. Tsalma knows that you always tease her, and you lasso her when she doesn't want to play. She might jump at you, Isak, because she is afraid you will bother her puppies."

Tsalma has come out, and Isak tries to sneak past her into the tent, but Tsalma bars his way and growls again.

Isak draws back and starts crying. "Please let me see the little puppies. Please let me see the little puppies! Isak will not lasso the little puppies!"

Anna looks out of the tent.

"Wait a moment," she says to Isak, "I will bring one out to you."

"Here is a puppy, Isak," says Anna.

The puppy is brown and has a white spot under her chin, just like Tsalma. Tsalma has come to the tent entrance again. She watches Isak and she watches her puppy. She still doesn't trust Isak; he has lassoed her too often. Isak stands a few steps away from the puppy.

"Isak does *not* lasso puppy," he calls to Tsalma—but he keeps at a safe distance.

I take him on my shoulders and dance around with him, and we two yoik together:

"Four puppies are born to Tsalma!" I sing.

"Voia Voia Nana," Isak yoiks.

"Four beautiful little puppies!"

"Voia Voia Nana!"

"Who will get a puppy?"

"Isak gets ALL puppies!" Isak answers.

Mother has come over and has looked at the puppies too. She sits down with Marit and watches us dancing around and yoiking, and she says, "Marit gets a puppy."

"Voia Nana Nana!" we shout.

"And Berit gets a little puppy," Eddny says.

"Voia Nana, Voia Nana!"

"Anna gets a little puppy!"

"Voia Voia Nana!" we yoik again. But Isak doesn't yoik any more. He looks as if he wants to cry again.

"And little Isak gets a puppy!" Eddny says. And Isak shouts with all his might:

"Isak Isak Isak! Isak gets a little puppy!"

"Voia Voia Nana!" we answer.

"But Anna will take care of the puppy first, and Isak promises never to lasso it!" Eddny says, and Isak promises.

5

IT IS FOUR WEEKS since we pitched our tents on the bank of the great fjord. The sun has not gone down at night for ten days now, and it will stay above the horizon for another forty days.

"The skins in the brook will be ready for plucking, Anders," says Eddny. "Let's go and take them out."

We walk over the marshy meadows and through the birch woods until we come to the little stream. Six skins lie in it, furry side up. I walk into the water to drag the skins out. They are held down by heavy stones, so they can't swim away. I take the stones up and get the skins.

Eddny and I pluck the hair off in big tufts. It comes off easily after the long soaking, and we put it into leather bags. Later Eddny will dry the hair and stuff pillows with it, or sell it to Nils Helander in Kautokeino or to Heikki the trader.

We carry the hides back with us also, to soak in the barrel of bark water.

Before Eddny drops the skins into the barrel she stretches them, one after the other, over a board. With an iron scraper on a wooden roller she scrapes off the fat and the remaining hair.

After a few days the skins in the barrel will be soft leather ready to be made into breeches and summer boots. The sugar bags are made from it too, and the coffee bags and all our pouches.

Ellen and Inga have cleaned the pots and pans, and hung them on the nails in the pantry tree for drying. On another tree hang dried meat and fish heads, and everything else we want to keep out of reach of the dogs.

I cut some more wood for the fire and bring it to the tent. As I carry it inside a cloud of smoke hits my face and everybody in the tent begins to scream.

I drop the wood and rub my eyes. Through the smoke I see Berit and Anna covering their faces with their hands and crying with fright. Isak screams and runs toward me.

"My meat, Anders! My meat jumped in the fire!" he cries.

A huge chunk of sooty meat lies in the wet ashes of the hearth, as do an overturned pan and a pail. The fire has gone out and there is a little pool of water in the ashes. The girls are crying too—their faces are burned. Eddny has come running in.

"Stop crying, you three cooks," she says. "Lie down on the skins." She takes her knife from her belt and quickly cuts potatoes into thin slices. She smears fat on the children's faces and places the potato slices over it, on the aching spots.

"It will not hurt for long," Eddny says, "and you will not get any blisters. How did this happen, Anna—with you in the tent to take care of the younger ones?"

Anna says, "We wanted to surprise you and have a meal ready when you came back from the brook. We wanted to fry meat, and we put it in the frying pan."

"And then?"

"And then Berit wanted to hold the pan. She——"

"I held it with *both* hands!" Berit exclaims.

"Berit dropped it," says Isak.

"I did *not* drop it. I only held it too low. It was awfully heavy. And then it happened."

"Everything burned," says Isak.

"It did *not* burn," Anna interrupts. "I think we had too much fat in the pan, and the fat caught fire and started burning. And then Isak took the pail of water and poured it over the pan. And then——"

"Everything burned," Isak cries again.

"Now you be quiet, Isak," says Eddny. "Go on, Anna."

"And then the fat splashed, and Isak got frightened and dropped the whole pail of water into the pan, and then the fat really splashed about and burned our faces."

"Everybody burned," says Isak.

"Pouring water into fat! You should have known it would splatter," says Eddny. "Now lie quietly for a while and you will soon be all right, my potato faces!" She laughs, and I laugh. They look so funny.

I take out my *Polar Star*. It is five weeks old, and it has twelve pages. I have already read my newspaper several times, but I like reading it again. On the first page there is a story about a reindeer thief. I read it to Anna and Marit and Isak:

"A man was caught in Alta on the Arctic Sea with eighteen reindeer he had stolen. He says he took only one or two stray animals from each herd. The man says he had only a small herd of one hundred and twenty animals, and last winter he was unlucky and lost thirty-six animals to the wolves, and seventeen died of exhaustion. So he took other people's reindeer. He could no longer live on his small herd and would have had to give up being a nomad Lapp.

"The sheriff ordered him to take care of the eighteen stolen animals, and of any calves they may have in spring. He ordered him to drive his herd to the Kautokeino area in the fall. There the elders will sit in judgment and decide what to do with him. If he took the reindeer only because otherwise he would have to give up being a nomad Lapp, he may be allowed to keep the calves, but not the grown reindeer."

"But he stole them," says Anna.

Eddny explains to her, "We all know how hard it is to go on being a nomad Lapp if the herd gets too small. So if the man did not steal for greed one must have pity. We want our people to go on being reindeer nomads."

"But if a man steals anything from our tents?" asks Marit.

This time I answer: "Even if it is only an old lasso, he will surely be beaten up and brought to the sheriff and sentenced by the judges. It is the worst crime to steal from a tent."

Eddny takes the potato slices from the children's faces—no blisters have formed. Our mother is a good doctor. She always knows the right cure, even when somebody is really sick. But that rarely happens.

We never have a real doctor, and we all learn how to cure sickness with herbs we find on the fjells.

Inga and Ellen have come back, with little Johan in his cradle slung over Inga's shoulders. They have been out picking cloudberries.

Eddny rips off a page from her calendar.

"What does the calendar say today?" she asks Anna, and hands her the paper. There is a riddle on the front of the page, and the answer is on the back. The calendar has a riddle or saying for every day.

Anna looks at the calendar.

"Listen carefully, Berit and Isak," she says. "This is an easy riddle. Ten little men are taken prisoner every morning and put into a dark corner. There are no skins on the ground to sleep on comfortably, not even birch twigs—only a little senna grass. But every night the ten little men are let out again. What is it?"

Berit and Isak think hard, but they cannot find the answer. Inga helps them: "Isak sets his ten little prisoners free even during the day-time," she says.

"Isak's toes," says Berit.

"My little, little toes!" shouts Isak. He is very happy about the riddle, and takes off his boots to look at his ten little prisoners.

I hear Ran barking. I look through the tent flap and see Atche coming back from the fjells, the rocky hills where our reindeer graze. He went up yesterday to look after the does. He is carrying three big beautiful antlers, and his kofte is bulging.

We all go out to greet Atche, and Eddny asks, "Have all the does calved now?"

"Yes, Christine, all of them have calved," Atche answers, "and all the does have shed their antlers. Here are three I found on the fjells."

"Atche must have found a treasure on his way," says Inga. "Look at his bulging kofte."

Atche smiles. "No, I have not found a treasure, but I have brought something for each of you. I met Heikki the trader on my way." We are very curious, but Eddny says, "Let Atche rest and eat first."

I carry the three antlers over to the pile where all the others are heaped. I wonder what treasures Atche has bought from Heikki the trader. Heikki wanders all summer long over the fjells and viddas of

Lapland, his wares loaded on the backs of his two reindeer. He knows where everybody camps during the summer, and he brings news from one siida to the next.

In his bags he carries the best knives in the world. He has silk scarves for the women and girls, and dolls and toys and pepper and newspapers and watches and raisins. He has everything.

In the tent Atche eats and tells about the does and about Heikki. Then he reaches into the front opening of his kofte and brings out his treasures.

"This is for you, Christine," he says, and gives Eddny a beautiful knife. The leather sheath is decorated with silver, and the blade is of Swedish steel.

Eddny's old knife is jagged-edged from constant use all through the winter and spring. She is very happy with the new one, and hangs it on her belt at once.

"There is one for you, Inga." And Inga gets a new knife too, with a handle of foreign black wood. "May you cut your wedding cake with it," Atche says, and we all laugh. Inga answers, "Thank you, Atche, thank you!" and leaves the tent. She does not like it when we tease her about her coming wedding.

Now it is my turn, and Atche tosses me a knife with a horn handle, in a red leather sheath.

"Try it out, Anders," Atche says. "I think it is a very good blade." And I thank Atche.

Everybody gets a new knife today, even Isak. We need our knives all the time: for slicing thongs into the right shape, for cutting ropes, for carving meat, hacking twigs off the branches, whittling pegs for the reindeer harnesses, working the birch bark into boxes, and notching marks into the earlaps of the fawns at the roundup. We need knives for almost everything we do. They are our most precious possessions, apart from the reindeer.

I go outside, and Isak follows me with his new knife.

First I throw the knife at a mark on a tree to see whether it is built straight. It flies through the air like an arrow and its point quivers in the tree right on the mark. Fine! I hang it on a branch by a string and strike the blade with the edge of my old knife. The steel sounds a clear note: there is no hidden crack in the blade.

I strike at a thick branch with the knife. The blade cuts through the branch as if it were reindeer cheese. And now I test the point on a flat bone. I carve a reindeer into the surface. The point follows the pressure of the fingers like the thin paint brush I use for decorating the bone knives I make. It is the best knife I have ever had.

Isak looks on while I work on the bone with the point of my new knife. He starts yoiking now: "Look at my knife, my beautiful knife, voia, voia, voia!"

He hangs his knife on a branch and hits it with a stick.

"My knife does not sing, Anders," he complains. "Bad knife." I show Isak how to test the blade with another blade, and then he puts it back into the sheath. He runs off and comes back with one of the antlers Atche has brought home.

"Anders, make a big knife handle, please," he says.

"I will make one," I answer.

I hack off a piece from the antler just at the root. Then I cut it into the right shape for a knife handle. I stain it with birch-bark water, and then I cut a design into it.

I worked on the knife for several days. I painted two running reindeer on the piece of bone I have used for it. Now on each side of the reindeer I carve designs, which I copy from one of Atche's old knives.

Isak runs away again, and brings another antler from the pile.

"Isak can lasso all the reindeer," he says.

"Isak," I answer, "here is my lasso. If you can catch the antler on your first try I will give you the lasso. But you must walk thirty paces away from the antler."

"Isak can keep the lasso?" he asks.

"Yes."

Isak puts the antler down, then he turns and walks thirty paces away. He swings the lasso over his head, aims carefully, and throws. The lasso whirls through the air—and the antler is hooked.

"Let's play the roundup game," says Anna. "Isak, you are the herder, and we are the reindeer."

We all hold antlers to our foreheads and run around Isak. He finds it much harder to catch us than it was to catch the antler on the ground. We zigzag, and when we hear the lasso we jump sideways. Isak gives up. I take the lasso and catch Ellen.

In the end only Anna is left. Now *she* becomes the herder, and we start all over again.

Marit goes to her tent. "I am getting my Bible," she says. Marit loves to read her Bible. She sits by the tent with Tshupp beside her, and reads.

Suddenly Tsalma comes running and puts her paws on Marit's shoulders.

"What's the matter, Tsalma?" Marit asks. Tsalma whines and turns her head in the direction of the fjells. Marit goes to her tent, where the puppies are. But Tsalma does not follow. She stands still and growls toward the fjells. Marit comes back and says, "There is nothing wrong with the puppies. Tsalma must have seen or smelled something on the fjells she doesn't like. I wish I knew what it was."

"Tsalma looks like a big wolf now," says Berit.

Atche answers, "Do you not know the dogs lived wild like wolves in olden times? They hunted with the wolves. Then FEAR came into the world, and when the wild animals became afraid of each other they began to fight among themselves. The dogs were not as strong as the wolves. They were often beaten, and had to live on the scraps the wolves left them.

"One day a famished dog saw a herdsman running around his reindeer herd. The man had a hard time getting his herd together. He shouted, then barked at the reindeer. When the dog saw this, he went up to the herdsman and said, 'I can run much faster than you, and I can bark better. Would you like me to help you round up the reindeer?'

"The herdsman said, 'What do you want for your help?' and the dog answered, 'I want a bowl of reindeer soup every day when you have one. And I want to eat all the leftover scraps I can find around your tent. And I want two promises.'

" 'What are your wishes?' asked the herdsman.

" 'I shall never in my life be beaten,' said the dog, 'and when I am old my death shall be painless.'

"The herdsman agreed. The dog brought all the other wild dogs, and they have helped us with our reindeer ever since, and they defend our herds against the wolves. They have kept their promise, and have become our best friends. We have kept our promise, and have become *their* best friends."

Eddny has made coffee. I go to the provision tent to get a new bag of sugar. When I come back, my Uncle Nils is standing at the tent flap. He looks up to the hills, and his dog looks there too, and then he shouts, "Lemmings! Lemmings!"

Everybody comes running, and we look up at the hills.

"There they are!" cries Uncle Nils, and points. Through my telescope I quickly spot a horde of small animals running over the rocks like giant mice. They do not come down to us but make straight for the fjord, farther up. Soon they are out of sight.

68

"Why do the lemmings run to the coast?" Berit asks.

"Nobody knows for sure," Atche answers. "They are very strange animals. Every third or fourth year they increase about ten times, and then the food gets scarce, and they start migrating. Perhaps they are looking for better feeding grounds. They migrate by the thousands straight down to the coast. They swim the rivers, and go over every obstacle in their way. When they meet our reindeer herds, they rush right through. The reindeer get annoyed and frightened, and scatter all over the fjells. The lemmings cannot stop even when they come to the ocean. They plunge in and start swimming. They quickly become exhausted, and they all drown in the waves. It is strange and terrible to see the great hordes of lemmings dive into the sea as if they wanted to die."

Uncle Nils' camp is five hours away from ours. He tells us what happened.

"I was on the way to my herd, which is now grazing near yours. Through my telescope I saw your reindeer fawns scatter and hit out at something at their feet. It could only be lemmings. I turned and rushed down here. We must go at once and round up the herds again."

"More lemmings!" Isak cries. Now we see hundreds of them coming down.

The dogs get very excited. They want to chase the lemmings and eat them, but we hold them back. We must go up and look after the reindeer.

Inga's dog Benne runs off. Atche and I call our dogs and tell them to bring Benne back. Ran and Tshupp race after Benne and the three fight. Benne fights back, but Tshupp has him by the throat. He does not really bite him but forces him to give in, and Benne is driven back. He goes whining to Inga, and sits quietly beside her until we leave.

I stuff reindeer cheese and meat into my rucksack; Eddny carries the kettle and coffee and sugar.

We climb straight up into the mountains over the steep rocks. There is no time to go the easier way, across the slopes.

Higher up we walk over the fjells until we reach a high meadow. I take out my telescope, sit down, and steady it between the thumb of my left hand and a piece of wood. Then I scan the hills thoroughly.

On the opposite slope I see a young reindeer buck wandering alone over the bare rocks. But farther on the big herd is grazing undisturbed —the lemmings have not gone their way. The buck must have strayed from the big herd—and now I see him wander back toward it. We do not go there, but walk on to the small herd of does.

There, across a mountain stream, we see the lemmings again. Thousands of them swarm over the ground and devour every plant.

They come in our direction, but the stream is in their way. The lemmings jump in and swim across, and many are carried downstream and drown. The others climb up the bank and come directly toward us. The dogs bark wildly, but the lemmings do not run away. They stand up on their furry feet, bare their teeth, and give a hissing bark in return. Some even jump up at us, and they try to bite into my skallers. Marit and Berit are frightened, and we put them on our shoulders.

The dogs attack the lemmings furiously and the lemmings defend themselves, until the dogs have them between their teeth. The others rush on, down toward the coast.

I see a few lemmings carrying young ones between their teeth, and other young ones clinging to the backs of their parents.

We tear the dogs away from the lemmings and hurry on. Atche leads us across a valley and up a rocky hill, until we reach the plateau where only this morning he had seen the does and fawns grazing together.

"We are very lucky," Atche says. "Most of the fawns are still there. But the lemmings have disturbed them." We count the fawns. Eight are missing, as well as four does.

A few lemmings are still running around. Two of them have found shelter under a rock. One stands up and hisses at me when I pass.

Through my telescope I see a few fawns running toward the snow fields.

"There are dangerous crevasses over there," says Atche. "Let us hurry."

One by one we find the does and the fawns, and lead them back to the herd. One fawn is still missing. At last Ellen and Anna wave to us from a ridge and signal to us that they have found it. It has fallen into a deep crevasse.

Atche puts his lasso around my waist and makes it fast with a knot. He and Eddny hold the lasso. Slowly I creep forward to the crevasse, and then they let me down. I grab the fawn and shout, "I have it!"

Atche and Eddny pull me up again and the fawn hobbles with us, back to the others.

It is midnight when we sit down at last, and make coffee over an open fire. The sun has been standing near the horizon for hours, and in its mild light we see our reindeer grazing peacefully on the fjells around us.

We drink the coffee, dipping dried reindeer meat in it. Then Uncle Nils goes his way, and we descend over rocks and slopes to our tents.

We walk along the shore of the fjord. Everything is lit by the pale gold rays of the midnight sun.

Soon the summer will be over. In fall, we will wander over the fjells and get our reindeer together again at the big roundup.

When the first snow falls the winter trek will begin, back through the fjords and rivers, over frozen lakes, and then high up over the mountains, and on and on, until we reach the snow fields of our winter village.

GLOSSARY

Bannugakko	Our pancake. It is made of flour mixed with reindeer blood.
Bazza derivan	"Stay in peace." We say this to someone who stays behind.
Boasso	The place in the tent where only Mother sits.
Buore Baive	"Good day."
Buurist	"God save you." We say this when we part or meet.
Dappat	"Shut up!"
Fjells	The rocky hills of my country.
Fjord	A narrow inlet from the ocean cutting into the land. There are fjords all along the coast.
Kautokeino	The name of our church village where we stay for the four winter months.
Kofte	The long blue blouse we wear. It is made of thick wool, and ribbons of yellow and red and blue are sewn on it.
Mana derivan	"Go in peace!" We say this to someone who is going away.
Nuorttanaste	*Polar Star.* This is the name of our newspaper in the Samic language.
Puuko	My long knife. I killed the wolf with it.
Raido	The caravan of our sledges and reindeer on migration.
Samer	Our name for ourselves. But other people call us Lapps.
Senna grass	It grows along the banks of the fjords. We cut it in summer and dry it, and then we use it instead of socks.
Siida	Our family, our reindeer, our dogs and tents—all these together are called a siida.
Skallers	My boots, made of reindeer skin.
Vidda	The moss-covered plateaus of Lapland over which we travel during migration.
Yoiking	This is when I sing, and make up my own words to go with one of our melodies.

The authors wish to thank Mr. Gunnar Rosenvinge Nygaard of Tromsoe for his untiring assistance in our search of the nomad Lapps. We also acknowledge gratefully the co-operation of the following photographers: Ekholtz, Olander Ehemgen (22, 31, 37), Fritz Goro (74), Mrs. Kittle-Parker (75), Davis Pratt (5, 6, 9, 19, 21).

Maps drawn by Anne Marie Jauss